Focus on Phonics-2a   by G

Short Vowel Sounds

Student Workbook

Correlated to
Laubach Way to Reading
Skill Book 2

ISBN 0-88336-447-6

© Copyright 1979, 1982 (revised), 1991

New Readers Press
Division of ProLiteracy Worldwide
1320 Jamesville Ave., Syracuse, New York 13210

Designed by Kay Koschnick and Ann Tussing

Illustrated by Caris Lester and Chris Steenwerth

Printed in the United States of America

20 19 18 17 16 15 14

Do They Rhyme?

Look at the pictures and say the words.
Do the words rhyme?
Make a check ☑ in the box if they do.

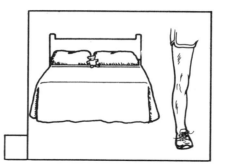

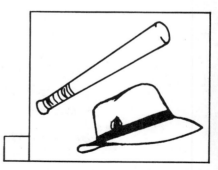

Two Forms of the Letter a

1

$$a = a$$

at   at

and   and

man   man

has   has

2 Circle all the words that are spelled the same as the first one.

an	an on an in and an
are	and are an are at are
at	at in at is on at
has	his has hand has has her
pan	an pan pat hand pan Pam

3 Write these words.

an   *an*

are   _____

pan   _____

hand _____

apple _____

thank _____

4 Read these sentences.

1. The man has a pan in his hand.

2. Cal looks at the girl's hands.

3. Dan and Ann are at Pam's shop.

4. Cal has a quarter for Dan.

5. Sam gives an apple to Van.

   Van thanks Sam.

3

1

Jill

Hill

Will

-ill

2 Write the letter or letters and say the word.

		ill			ch ____ ill
b	____	ill		B ____ ill
f	____	ill		H ____ ill
h	____	ill		J ____ ill
k	____	ill		W ____ ill
m	____	ill		
p	____	ill		
t	____	ill		
w	____	ill		

3 Read the words.

pill	hill
mill	Jill
fill	Will
bill	Hill
will	Bill
ill	
chill	
kill	
till	

4 Write the word you hear.

1. _____   10. _____

2. _____   11. _____

3. _____   12. _____

4. _____   13. _____

5. _____   14. _____

6. _____

7. _____

8. _____

9. _____

5

Review Words

it

sister

Words from Skill Book 1

a	he	not
are	his	on
at	is	she
cup	Liz	snake
for	man	the
get	Mr.	this
has	Mrs.	up

6 Read the sentences.

1. Fill it up.

2. The mill is on the hill.

3. Will she get a chill?

4. This is Mr. Will Hill.

5. Is he ill?

6. This bill is for his sister.

7. Will the man kill the snake?

   He will not kill it.

8. Jill has a bill for the pills.

9. Liz is not his sister.

10. She will fill the cups.

11. Bill is up on the hill.

12. The pills are for his sister.

13. Chill it till 3.

14. Mrs. Hill has a sister.

15. Will he get a bill for it?

16. Bill is at the mill till 6.

17. Jill has a chill. She is ill.

Practice 1-B: Word Family -ick

1

kick

pick

-ick

2 Write the letter or letters and say the word.

k ___ ick   D ___ ick

l ___ ick   N ___ ick

p ___ ick   R ___ ick

s ___ ick

t ___ ick

w ___ ick

qu ___ ick

ch ___ ick

th ___ ick

3 Read the words.

sick   Dick

tick   pick

wick   thick

Nick

lick

kick

chick

Rick

quick

4 Write the word you hear.

1. _____   10. _____

2. _____   11. _____

3. _____   12. _____

4. _____

5. _____

6. _____

7. _____

8. _____

9. _____

5

Review Words

gift
big
little

New Words

me
we

Words from Skill Book 1

an   hand   pup
and   have   to
apple

6 Read the sentences.

1. Nick is not sick.

2. We have a little chick.

3. Quick! Pick it up!

4. The pup will lick his hand.

5. Kick it to me.

6. It is not thick.

7. Will we get sick?

8. Dick picks up the bill for the gift.

9. It ticks and ticks.

10. The big pup licks the little pup.

11. Chill it till it gets thick.

12. Nick will pick an apple.

13. The pups have ticks.

14. The little chicks are quick.

15. Rick kicks me.

16. Pick a gift for me.

17. We have pills for the sick man.

18. Dick and Rick have a mill.

5

1

big

-ig

Miss

-iss

his

-is

2 Write the letter or letters and say the word.

b _____ ig   h _____ iss

d _____ ig   k _____ iss

p _____ ig   m _____ iss

w _____ ig   M _____ iss

                    is

                    h _____ is

                    th _____ is

3 Read the words.

wig   Miss

big   hiss

pig   kiss

dig   miss

his   this

is

4 Write the word you hear.

1. _____   9. _____

2. _____   10. _____

3. _____

4. _____   11. _____

5. _____

6. _____

7. _____

8. _____

5

Review Words

little

Words from Skill Book 1

girl
give
her
I
you

6 Read the sentences.

1. This is Miss Jill Hill.

2. This wig is thick.

3. Dig it up.

4. I miss you.

5. The snake will hiss.

6. It is little, not big.

7. He will kiss Miss Hill.

8. The pigs are not his.

9. Will you miss me?

10. Is this pig sick?

11. Will you kiss Jill's big sister?

12. Nick and I hiss at Bill.

13. This wig is big for you.

14. Rick digs on the hill.

15. I give her a big kiss.

16. Dick will miss his girl.

17. The pig is big, and the chick is little.

18. Bill gets a wig for his girl.

1

it

sit

-it

2 Write the letter or letters and say the word.

	it	qu ____ it
b	____ it	
f	____ it	
h	____ it	
k	____ it	
l	____ it	
p	____ it	
s	____ it	
w	____ it	

3 Read the words.

kit   fit

sit

it

quit

lit

wit

hit

pit

bit

4 Write the word you hear.

1. _____   10. _____

2. _____

3. _____

4. _____

5. _____

6. _____

7. _____

8. _____

9. _____

5

Review Words

with

New Words

your

Words from Skill Book 1

in   dish
put   shop
of   olive
leg

6 Read the sentences.

1. I will dig a big pit.

2. She will quit.

3. Will the wig fit me?

4. Your pup bit the girl.

5. The shop is lit up.

6. Your sister sits with Rick.

7. Pick up this kit.

8. He has a quick wit.

9. Hit it with your hand.

10. The little pup bit his leg.

11. The sick man sits up.

12. It will not fit in the kit.

13. I will not quit till 6.

14. Put the olive pits in the dish.

15. It is little, and it will not fit me.

16. She is a girl with a wit.

17. He hits and kicks the man.

18. Give me a little bit of it.

7

1

in

-in

Kim

him

-im

2 Write the letter or letters and say the word.

	in	th _____ in
b _____ in		
f _____ in	d _____ im	
p _____ in	h _____ im	
s _____ in	r _____ im	
t _____ in	J _____ im	
w _____ in	K _____ im	
ch _____ in	T _____ im	
sh _____ in		

3 Read the words.

tin	pin
sin	
in	Kim
shin	him
bin	Jim
chin	dim
win	Tim
thin	rim
fin	

4 Write the word you hear.

1. _____   10. _____
2. _____
3. _____   11. _____
4. _____   12. _____
5. _____   13. _____
6. _____   14. _____
7. _____   15. _____
8. _____   16. _____
9. _____

5

Review Words

dinner

New Words

into

Words from Skill Book 1

fish
quarter
they

6 Read the sentences.

1. A fish has fins.

2. I put a quarter into the man's tin cup.

3. Will they win it?

4. Jim and Tim have dinner.

   They have dinner with Kim.

5. I kick him in the shin.

6. Jim bit into an apple.

7. Kim is thin.

8. It is a sin to kill.

9. Jim has a big chin.

10. A pin is thin, not thick.

11. This is the rim of the cup.

12. They will not quit till they win.

13. It is dim in the mill.

14. The apples are in the bin.

15. Kim hit him on the chin.

16. Put the tin pins into this kit.

17. Tim gets a hit and wins.

Practice 2-C: Word Families -ing, -ink

1

sing

ring

-ing

sink

rink

-ink

2 Write the letter or letters and say the word.

k ____ ing   ink

r ____ ing   l ____ ink

s ____ ing   m ____ ink

w ____ ing   p ____ ink

th ____ ing   r ____ ink

br ____ ing   s ____ ink

                    w ____ ink

                    th ____ ink

3 Read the words.

ring   link

king   pink

thing   ink

sing   sink

bring   think

wing   wink

            mink

            rink

4 Write the word you hear.

1. _____   7. _____

2. _____   8. _____

3. _____   9. _____

4. _____   10. _____

5. _____   11. _____

6. _____   12. _____

            13. _____

            14. _____

5

Review Words

finger

New Words

drink

Words from Skill Book 1

bird   neck
live   one
look   street
my   telephone

6 Read the sentences.

1. This ink is pink.

2. She puts the drink in the cups.

   He drinks one cup of it.

3. The bird has big wings.

4. I think Will lives on this street.

5. Give me a mink, not a ring.

6. Bring the things to the sink.

7. The birds sing.

8. I get ink on my fingers.

9. He has a ring on his finger.

10. Jim is at the rink with Jill.

11. They will sing for the king.

12. Bill winks at girls.

13. The telephone rings.

14. The pink cup is in the sink.

15. I think my ring will fit her finger.

16. Bring me a drink.

17. He gives things to my sister.

9

Practice 2-D: Word Family -ip,

1

lip

zip

-ip

2 Write the letter or letters and say the word.

d ____ ip		sh ____ ip	
h ____ ip		ch ____ ip	
l ____ ip			
n ____ ip			
r ____ ip			
s ____ ip			
t ____ ip			
z ____ ip			
wh ____ ip			

3 Read the words.

nip	lip
chip	hip
zip	
rip	
dip	
sip	
whip	
tip	
ship	

4 Write the word you hear.

1. _____   10. _____

2. _____   11. _____

3. _____

4. _____

5. _____

6. _____

7. _____

8. _____

9. _____

5

New Words

our

Words from Skill Book 1

zipper
hurt

6 Read the sentences.

1. Jim licks his lips.

2. She hurt her hip.

3. Dip it into the cup.

4. Kim rips up the bills.

5. This is the tip of the pin.

6. Dick has a big whip in his hand.

   He will not hit the pup with the whip.

7. Our ship will not sink.

8. Zip up the zipper.

9. Our pup nips at Bill's leg.

10. She fills the dish with chips.

11. She picks up the cup and sips the drink.

12. This will not fit at the hips.

13. Tim will kiss her on the lips.

14. The pup bit the tip of my finger.

15. The chip dip is in the pink dish.

16. She zips it up, and it rips.

17. Our sister is on the ship.

Practice 3-A: Word Families -id, -ib, -ix

1

did

-id

rib

-ib

six

-ix

2 Write the letter or letters and say the word.

b _____ id   b _____ ib

d _____ id   r _____ ib

h _____ id

k _____ id   f _____ ix

l _____ id   m _____ ix

r _____ id   s _____ ix

3 Read the words.

rid	rib
hid	bib
lid	
bid	mix
kid	six
did	fix

4 Write the word you hear.

1. _____   7. _____

2. _____   8. _____

3. _____

4. _____   9. _____

5. _____   10. _____

6. _____   11. _____

5

Review Words

city
Kitty
whistle

New Words

want

Words from Skill Book 1

two
pan

6 Read the sentences.

1. Mr. Hill has six kids.

2. Put the lid on the pan.

3. Get rid of the pills.

4. We hid her whistle.

5. Kitty did not mix up the bills.

6. I want you to fix the sink.

7. Bill hits Jim in the ribs.

8. Mrs. Hill puts a bib on her kid.

9. They bid on the things they want.

10. I think the two things will mix.

11. The kids did not live in the city.

12. My sister has six wigs.

13. Kitty will fix our dinner.

14. Bill and I want ribs for dinner.

15. The lid did not fit on the pan.

16. Nick wants to get rid of his things.

17. He did not want to bid on it.

18. The man hid in the city.

11

Practice 3-B: Word Families -ish, -ich, -itch, -ive

1

dish
-ish
rich
-ich
pitch
-itch
give
live
-ive

2 Write the letter or letters and say the word.

d _____ ish   itch

f _____ ish   d _____ itch

w _____ ish   h _____ itch

                   p _____ itch

r _____ ich   w _____ itch

wh _____ ich

                   g _____ ive

                   l _____ ive

3 Read the words.

dish   hitch

wish   itch

fish   pitch

              witch

rich   ditch

which

              live

              give

4 Write the word you hear.

1. _____   6. _____

2. _____   7. _____

3. _____   8. _____

                      9. _____

4. _____   10. _____

5. _____

                      11. _____

                      12. _____

5

Review Words

kitchen

New Words

be
if

Words from Skill Book 1

river

6 Read the sentences.

1. Kim will fix fish in the kitchen.

2. He will hit and pitch.

3. They live on a ship on the river.

   Which river is it?

4. Did he dig this big ditch?

5. I will be rich if I get my wish.

6. This girl is not a witch.

7. I think he will be sick.

   If he gets sick, give him a pill.

8. My hands itch.

9. Our kids fish in the river.

10. Which dish is the chip dip in?

11. If you win it, you will be rich.

12. We wish we did not live in the city.

13. Give me a big dish for this fish.

14. Pitch it to me, and I will hit it.

15. Six kids hid in the ditch.

16. The rich man gives and gives.

Practice 3-C: Adding Endings

1 Adding -s to words to show that there is more than one

a shop   one girl

six shop<u>s</u>   two girl<u>s</u>

2 Add -s and read the word.

hill _____

chick _____

lip _____

thing _____

bill _____

wig _____

3 Add -s to the word. Fill in the blank. Read the sentence.

1. pig   He sells ten_____.

2. ring   Jill has three_____.

3. pin   Pick up the_____.

4. kid   Kim has two_____.

5. cup   I want six_____.

4 Adding -s to action words

    I   sing.
She   sing<u>s</u>.
Jill   sing<u>s</u>.

We   kick.
He   kick<u>s</u>.
Jim   kick<u>s</u>.

You   sit.
  It   sit<u>s</u>.
The pup sit<u>s</u>.

5 Add -s and read the word.

pick _____

dig _____

win _____

live _____

think _____

put _____

6 Add -s to the word. Fill in the blank. Read the sentence.

1. bring   He_____me gifts.

2. fill   She_____up her cup.

3. lick   The pup_____my hands.

4. wink   Bill_____at Kim.

5. fit   The ring_____Jim's finger.

7 Adding -ing to action words

sing   We are sing<u>ing</u>.

think   I am think<u>ing</u>.

fish   He is fish<u>ing</u>.

8 Add -ing and read the word.

fill _____

mix _____

fish _____

bring _____

drink _____

pitch _____

9 Add -ing to the word. Fill in the blank. Read the sentence.

1. kiss   Tim is_____his girl.

2. sink   The ship is_____.

3. chill   Kim is_____the drink.

4. sing   Dick and Bill are_____.

5. fix   Jill is_____the sink.

13

Practice 3-D: Review Lesson - Short i

1 Look at the picture and say the word.
Then fill in the right letter to make the word.

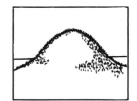

h
m ___ill

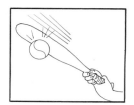

hi ___ t
       p

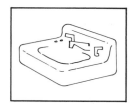

si ___ nk
        ck

d
b ___ ig

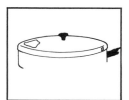

r
l ___ id

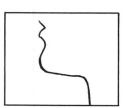

chi ___ n
         p

---

2 Circle the word that makes sense in the sentence.

1. I lick / lit my lips.

2. Did Tim wing / wink at Jill?

3. I think I will fix bibs / ribs for dinner.

4. Mix up this dip for the chips / ships .

5. Mrs. Hill will kiss / kit the children.

6. If Dick sells his digs / pigs , he will be rich.

3 Look at the picture and say the word.
Then circle the right word.

1.   rib   bib   did   bid

2.   lit   bit   hit   fit

3.   sip   sick   sit   six

4.   bill   pill   till   hill

5.   wick   wing   will   wink

6.   shin   ship   hip   chip

14

4 Look at the picture and say the word. Then write the word under the picture.

 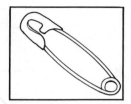 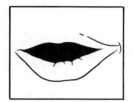   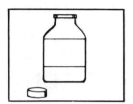

_____ _____ _____ _____ _____ _____

---

5 Circle all the words that are the same as the first.
Work from left to right.

pit	bit	pit	fit	pill	pit	tip	pit
bid	bid	big	did	bid	lid	hid	bid
hill	mill	lid	hill	bill	hill	kill	hit
fin	fix	fin	fin	fit	pin	fin	tin
nip	pin	whip	nip	hip	nip	pin	rip
lick	lick	kick	kill	live	lick	tick	lid
dig	big	dig	dip	dig	pig	big	did
ring	ring	rim	rink	ring	bring	rig	ring

6 Read these sentences.

1. Kim will fill up six cups with the drink.

2. Bill picks up the big dish and brings it to the sink.

3. His finger is thin, and the ring will not fit on it.

4. If Jim hits and you pitch, we will win!

5. I wish you did not have to quit. We will miss you.

6. If Mr. King gets sick with a chill, give him this pill.

7. Which city did Rick live in?

8. Whip the mix till it gets thick.

Practice 4-A: Word Families -un, -um

1

run

gun

sun

-un

gum

-um

2 Write the letter or letters and say the word.

b _____ un   b _____ um

f _____ un   g _____ um

g _____ un   h _____ um

n _____ un   r _____ um

r _____ un   s _____ um

s _____ un

3 Read the words.

nun	gum
sun	rum
gun	bum
run	hum
bun	sum
fun	

4 Write the word you hear.

1. _____   7. _____

2. _____   8. _____

3. _____   9. _____

4. _____   10. _____

5. _____   11. _____

6. _____

5

Review Words

son
hunt

New Words

out

Words from Skill Book 1

Ann   do
children sell

6 Read the sentences.

1. Kim will sing, and I will hum.

2. He puts the fish on a bun.

3. My son thinks it is fun to hunt.

   He is out hunting with his gun.

4. The man is a bum.

5. Do they sell gum in this shop?

6. Sister Ann is a nun.

7. The sum of 2 and 4 is 6.

8. Run and get my gun.

9. He has a drink of rum.

10. Is the sun up?

11. The nun hums and sings.

12. The children have fun out in the sun.

13. Do not run with a gun in your hand.

14. Sum it up for me.

15. My son puts the buns in the dish.

16. He wants me to give him gum.

    I do not have gum. I have run out of it.

Practice 4-B: Word Families -up, -ub, -us, -uss

1
cup
pup
-up
rub
-ub
bus
-us
fuss
-uss

2 Write the letter or letters and say the word.

	up			us
c	____ up	b	____ us
p	____ up	th	____ us
c	____ ub	c	____ uss
r	____ ub	f	____ uss
t	____ ub		

3 Read the words.

up	bus
cup	us
pup	thus
rub	fuss
tub	cuss
cub	

4 Write the word you hear.

1. _____   7. _____
2. _____   8. _____
3. _____   9. _____
4. _____   10. _____
5. _____   11. _____
6. _____

5

Review Words

son
hunt

New Words

husband
just

Words from Skill Book 1

go   tell   woman
jump   under

6 Read the sentences.

1. The woman fills up the tub.

2. He rubs the pup's neck.

3. My husband is picking up our pup.

4. Put the cups in the sink.

5. Just six of us will go on this bus.

6. The woman rubs her hands.

7. Do not cuss at us!

8. The little cubs jump and run.

9. The kids will fuss if they do not go with us.

10. The pups run under the bus.

11. My husband is sick. Thus, he will not go with us.

12. The woman has just two cups.

13. My husband runs up the street to get the bus.

    He will just miss his bus.

14. The woman sits in the tub.

15. If your leg hurts, rub it.

16. The woman tells her husband, "Do not fuss at me."

17. Did the Cubs win?

17

Practice 4-C: Word Families -ut, -ud, -uff

1

cut

-ut

mud

-ud

puff

-uff

2 Write the letter or letters and say the word.

b	____ ut	b	____ ud
c	____ ut	m	____ ud
h	____ ut	B	____ ud
r	____ ut		
n	____ ut	c	____ uff
sh	____ ut	m	____ uff
		p	____ uff

3 Read the words.

hut	Bud
rut	mud
nut	bud
but	
shut	puff
cut	muff
	cuff

4 Write the word you hear.

1. _____   7. _____
2. _____   8. _____
3. _____   9. _____
4. _____
5. _____   10. _____
6. _____   11. _____
                 12. _____

5

Review Words

duck
hunt
Jimmy

Words from Skill Book 1

box
no

6 Read the sentences.

1. Cut up the duck for us.

2. Jimmy gets mud on his cuff.

3. She shut up the shop.

4. Kitty is looking at the little pink buds.

   The buds are little, but they will get big.

5. Bill has no cuts on his hands.

6. The man lives in a hut.

   The hut has mud on it.

7. The woman gives nuts and gum to the kids.

8. I want to hunt ducks, but I have no gun.

9. Bud will not shut the box.

10. She puts her hands into the muff.

11. He gets a cut on his lip.

    His lip will puff up and get big.

12. The bus is in a big rut, but we will get it out.

13. We had fun hunting for nuts.

14. The woman tells the kids to shut up.

15. No one but Jill gets cut.

1

rug

jug

-ug

judge

-udge

2 Write the letter or letters and say the word.

b _____ ug   b _____ udge

d _____ ug   f _____ udge

h _____ ug   j _____ udge

j _____ ug   n _____ udge

m _____ ug

r _____ ug

t _____ ug

3 Read the words.

hug	fudge
tug	nudge
mug	budge
bug	judge
jug	
dug	
rug	

4 Write the word you hear.

1. _____   8. _____

2. _____   9. _____

3. _____   10. _____

4. _____   11. _____

5. _____

6. _____

7. _____

5

New Words

water

6 Read the sentences.

1. The woman hugs her son.

2. The jug has rum in it.

3. Is he a judge?

4. He tugs on the big rug.

5. The pup dug in the mud.

6. Put the water in a mug, not in a cup.

   Fill the mug with water.

7. I give Bud a nudge.

8. A big bug is under the rug.

9. Bill gives Kim a box of fudge.

   The fudge has nuts in it.

10. I hug and kiss my husband.

11. He will judge the pigs.

12. My son tugs on my hand.

13. I tug on the box, but it will not budge.

14. This cup of water has a bug in it.

15. Her pup gets mud on the rug.

16. He drinks out of the water jug.

1

duck
Buck
-uck

rush
-ush

much
-uch

2 Write the letter or letters and say the word.

b ___ uck	g ___ ush
d ___ uck	h ___ ush
l ___ uck	r ___ ush
s ___ uck	m ___ ush
t ___ uck	
st ___ uck	m ___ uch
tr ___ uck	s ___ uch
B ___ uck	
Ch ___ uck	

3 Read the words.

tuck	mush
luck	hush
buck	gush
stuck	rush
Chuck	
duck	such
suck	much
truck	
Buck	

4 Write the word you hear.

1. _____   10. _____
2. _____   11. _____
3. _____   12. _____
4. _____   13. _____
5. _____
6. _____   14. _____
7. _____   15. _____
8. _____
9. _____

5

Review Words

does
from
come
some

New Words

so
good

Words from Skill Book 1

thank
visit

6 Read the sentences.

1. Bud Buck comes from the city in his truck.

   Does his truck get stuck in the mud?

2. Kitty is fixing me some ducks for dinner.

   I tell her, "Thanks so much for such a good dinner."

3. Tuck it in.

4. Bud has such good luck.

5. He sells us some apples for two bucks.

6. Do not rush so much!

7. It is so good to have Chuck come to visit us.

8. Sam and Jim rush out of the shop.

9. Do not put so much mush in my dish.

   I just want a little.

10. The gum gets stuck on my fingers.

11. Mrs. Buck tells her children to hush.

12. He does not have good luck fixing trucks.

13. The fudge is stuck to the pan.

14. The little girl sucks on her finger.

15. Chuck has good luck hunting. He gets a big buck.

Practice 5-B: Word Families -ung, -unk

1

sung

-ung

sunk

junk

-unk

2 Write the letter or letters and say the word.

h _____ ung   b _____ unk

l _____ ung   d _____ unk

r _____ ung   h _____ unk

s _____ ung   j _____ unk

                            p _____ unk

                            s _____ unk

                            ch _____ unk

3 Read the words.

rung   junk

hung   sunk

sung   hunk

lung   bunk

              chunk

              dunk

              punk

4 Write the word you hear.

1. _____   5. _____

2. _____   6. _____

3. _____   7. _____

4. _____   8. _____

                        9. _____

                       10. _____

                       11. _____

5

Review Words

funny
mother
brother
uncle
picture
word

New Words

other
like

6 Read the sentences.

1. My brother likes to sit on his bunk.

2. Uncle Bud will get rid of the junk.

3. Dunk it under the water.

4. Mother hung up one other picture.

5. My brother Chuck has sung for us.

   We like the funny words he has sung.

6. A fish has no lungs.

7. Bill likes to dunk his sister in the water.

   The little punk thinks it is funny!

8. This hunk of tin is no good to us.

   Put it with the other junk.

9. The ship has sunk under the water.

10. Mother cuts a big chunk of fudge.

11. The picture from my uncle looks like junk to us.

    It looks funny, so we have not hung it up.

12. The telephone has rung. Did she get it?

    She did pick it up, but they hung up.

13. I want this bunk, not the other one.

21

Practice 5-C: Adding Endings

1 Adding *-ing* to VCC words

V C C + i n g

h u n t + i n g → hunting

f i l l + i n g → filling

t h i n k + i n g → thinking

2 Label the last three letters.
Write the word with *-ing*.

jump _____

kiss _____

fish _____

bring _____

3 Add *-ing* to the word.
Read the sentences.

drink 1. Are you _____ this?

hurt 2. Bud's leg is _____ him.

dunk 3. He is _____ it in water.

---

4 Adding *-ing* to CVC words

C V C + C + i n g

r u n + n + i n g → running

s h i p + p + i n g → shipping

h u m + m + i n g → humming

5 Label the last three letters.
Write the word with *-ing*.

hug _____

bid _____

dig _____

dip _____

6 Add *-ing* to the word.
Read the sentences.

hug 1. Mother is _____ her kids.

shut 2. She is _____ up the shop.

run 3. Dick is _____ up the hill.

7

Label the last three letters with VCC or CVC.
Write the word with *-ing*. Read the word.

rush _____   lick _____   fill _____

bud _____   want _____   rub _____

get _____   chill _____   rush _____

pick _____   cut _____   tip _____

8

Take off the *-ing*. Write the root word.
For some words you may have to take
off a letter.

ripping _____

pinning _____

shutting _____

fussing _____

wishing _____

Practice 5-D: Contrasting Short Vowels i and u

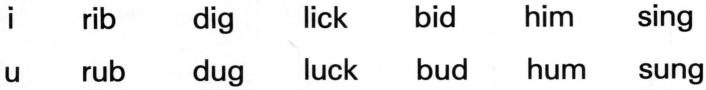

i	rib	dig	lick	bid	him	sing
u	rub	dug	luck	bud	hum	sung

---

1 Write the letter.

1. fin
   fun
   f __ n

2. rig
   rug
   r __ g

3. sin
   sun
   s __ n

4. hit
   hut
   h __ t

5. sink
   sunk
   s __ nk

2 Circle the word that you hear.

1. big   bug
2. lick   luck
3. rib   rub
4. miss   muss
5. bin   bun
6. him   hum
7. bit   but
8. chick   chuck
9. rim   rum
10. hitch   hutch
11. dig   dug
12. sick   suck
13. this   thus
14. pin   pun
15. ring   rung

3 Write the short vowel that you hear.

1. t ___ ck
2. s ___ p
3. th ___ nk
4. m ___ ff
5. p ___ g
6. b ___ d
7. s ___ ng
8. j ___ g
9. h ___ nk
10. f ___ zz
11. p ___ t
12. r ___ t
13. c ___ d
14. ch ___ n
15. s ___ ch

4 Circle the right word.

1. She will ___ her hands.
   rib
   rub

2. Bring me the ___ dish.
   pink
   punk

3. The pup ___ my leg.
   bit
   but

4. We wish him good ___ .
   lick
   luck

5. I sing and ___ to the children.
   him
   hum

6. The ___ is on her finger.
   ring
   rung

23

Practice 5-E: Review Lesson - Short U

1 Look at the picture and say the word.
Then fill in the right letter to make the word.

h
r __ ug

n
bu __
m

ff
pu __
p

t
cu __
b

l
p __ uck

f
j __ udge

---

2 Circle the word that makes sense in the sentence.

1. A bug bit his hand. Did his hand __ up?
   puck
   puff

2. Do not __ the mud on the rug.
   rub
   cub

3. Bud put the box under his __
   buck
   bunk

4. The __ is stuck on my hands.
   hum
   gum

5. Has she __ for us?
   sung
   sunk

6. The bum is drinking some __
   rum
   run

---

3 Look at the picture and say the word.
Then circle the right word.

1.    mug   hug   jug   rug

2.    puff   cut   cuff   cuss

3.    sung   sun   sum   sunk

4.    buzz   bus   buck   but

5. 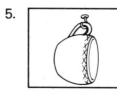   cub   up   cut   cup

6.    nut   run   nun   fun

24

4 Look at the picture and say the word. Then write the word under the picture.

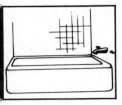 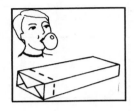    

_____ _____ _____ _____ _____ _____

---

5 Circle all the words that are the same as the first.
Work from left to right.

tug	lug	tug	tub	gut	tug	hug	tug
bud	bud	but	dub	bud	dud	bid	bug
cut	tuck	out	cut	cub	rut	put	cut
gum	gun	hum	gum	bum	mug	gum	gun
luck	luck	lung	lick	tuck	luck	look	buck
run	sun	nun	run	rum	run	rung	run
bus	bun	bus	sub	pus	bus	us	sub
pup	pub	pup	cup	dud	pug	pup	puff

6 Read these sentences.

1. Mrs. Buck puts one cup of nuts in the fudge.

2. Chuck's bus is stuck in a big rut.

   But my uncle will get it out with the truck.

3. The kids fuss until Mother says, "Hush!"

4. I hung up a picture of my uncle. He is a judge.

5. This rug is not much good. Put it out with the junk.

6. We had such fun hunting and fishing.

7. I rush up to my son and hug him.

1

yell

sell

well

-ell

2 Write the letter or letters and say the word.

b _____ ell   N _____ ell

f _____ ell

h _____ ell

s _____ ell

t _____ ell

w _____ ell

y _____ ell

sh _____ ell

B _____ ell

3 Read the words.

well   yell

bell

sell

hell

tell

Bell

shell

Nell

fell

4 Write the word you hear.

1. _____   10. _____

2. _____

3. _____

4. _____

5. _____

6. _____

7. _____

8. _____

9. _____

5

Review Words

help
twelve
very
fresh
many

New Words

until
jelly

Words from Skill Book 1

egg
seven

6 Read the sentences.

1. The woman tells us she has twelve children.

2. Mr. Bell has many fresh eggs to sell.

   He sells us a box of twelve fresh eggs.

3. I will help the sick man until he gets well.

4. Bud yells to Mr. Bell, "Help! Help!"

5. She fell and hurt her leg.

6. We will not have dinner until seven.

7. Nell picks up many shells from the water.

8. The woman sings very well.

9. The bell will ring at twelve.

10. He does not want to go to hell.

11. She yells, but no one comes to help.

12. Get the nut out of the shell.

13. Nell sells very good jelly at her shop.

    Bud tells us to get some apple jelly from her.

14. The little girl fell into a big well.

15. Tell your brother not to yell at me.

16. The children yell until the bell rings.

Practice 6-B: Word Family -et

1

get

pet

-et

2 Write the letter or letters and say the word.

b _____ et   w _____ et

g _____ et   y _____ et

j _____ et

l _____ et

m _____ et

n _____ et

p _____ et

s _____ et

v _____ et

3 Read the words.

set   met

pet   jet

net

yet

get

vet

let

wet

bet

4 Write the word you hear.

1. _____   10. _____

2. _____   11. _____

3. _____

4. _____

5. _____

6. _____

7. _____

8. _____

9. _____

5

Review Words

cents

seventy

New Words

any   there

must   TV

Words from Skill Book 1

says

yes

6 Read the sentences.

1. Jimmy says a pup is a very good pet.

2. Mr. Bell will get on a big jet.

3. Set the eggs there.

4. Have you met my brother yet?

5. Mother will not let the kids look at TV.

6. Are there any fish in the net?

7. He must rush his pet to the vet.

    The vet will set the pup's leg.

8. Bill will bet seventy cents.

9. Yes, he met her there for dinner.

10. I must sell my TV set.

11. The pup jumps into the tub and gets wet.

12. He does not let the children have any pets.

13. You must fix the net if you want to get any fish.

14. I bet he will not get there until twelve.

15. The sun has not set yet.

16. Yes, let us go there on a jet.

17. I do not want to bet.

27

1

hen

ten

men

-en

neck

-eck

2 Write the letter or letters and say the word.

d ___ en   d ___ eck

h ___ en   n ___ eck

m ___ en   p ___ eck

p ___ en   ch ___ eck

t ___ en

th ___ en

wh ___ en

B ___ en

K ___ en

3 Read the words.

men	peck
ten	neck
Ben	check
hen	deck
den	
pen	
then	
Ken	
when	

4 Write the word you hear.

1. _____   10. _____

2. _____   11. _____

3. _____   12. _____

4. _____   13. _____

5. _____

6. _____

7. _____

8. _____

9. _____

5

Review Words

cents
twelve

New Words

women

Words from Skill Book 1

four   tent
Glenn   write
Pam

6 Read the sentences.

1. The deck of the ship is wet.

2. Pam is a woman. Pam and Ann are women.

   Ken is a man. Ken and Ben are men.

3. Glenn writes a check for the TV set.

4. Ken is sitting in his den with two men.

5. This pen is just ten cents, but it writes well.

6. If the bus does not run, then the men will check it.

7. The chick pecks at the egg to get out of it.

   The little chick will get to be a big hen.

8. When Ben is four, then Ken will be ten.

9. When will the dinner be? At seven.

   Twelve men and ten women are coming then.

10. Ben's neck hurts.

11. The little cubs live in the den.

12. The women write checks when they shop.

13. Ten big hens are in the pen.

14. Does the tent have a rip? Check it.

15. Men and women are sitting on the deck.

Practice 7-A: Word Families -eg, -ess

1

leg

-eg

less

-ess

2 Write the letter or letters and say the word.

	egg	gu ____	ess
b ____	eg	l ____	ess
k ____	eg	m ____	ess
l ____	eg	ch ____	ess
p ____	eg	B ____	ess
M ____	eg	J ____	ess
P ____	eg		

3 Read the words.

peg	mess
leg	Bess
egg	guess
keg	less
Peg	Jess
beg	chess
Meg	

4 Write the word you hear.

1. _____   8. _____
2. _____   9. _____
3. _____   10. _____
4. _____   11. _____
5. _____   12. _____
6. _____   13. _____
7. _____

5

Review Words

quickly
pretty
them

New Words

best
dress
make
unless

Words from Skill Book 1

address
nest
valley

6 Read the sentences.

1. Meg will get the best dress at the shop.

   The dress is selling for much less.

2. Peg gives a chess set to them.

3. He will run unless his leg hurts.

4. You must have the pegs to put up the tent.

5. Jess is bringing a keg of rum.

6. I will have to guess unless you tell me.

7. Bess begs the kids not to make a mess.

8. Yes, I guess this box of eggs is the best.

9. Write your address on the check.

10. It is less windy in the valley.

11. Mother tells them to pick up the mess quickly.

12. Jess will get some eggs from the hens' nests.

13. Did Ken make the best guess?

14. I will not win at chess unless you help me.

15. Your dress makes you look very pretty.

16. The man begs them for a quarter.

17. Peg makes a mess in the kitchen.

29

1

Ed

bed

red

-ed

edge

ledge

-edge

2 Write the letter or letters and say the word.

b _____ ed   T _____ ed

f _____ ed

l _____ ed   edge

r _____ ed   h _____ edge

w _____ ed   l _____ edge

sh _____ ed   w _____ edge

Ed

Fr _____ ed

N _____ ed

3 Read the words.

led   Fred

wed

shed   hedge

Ed   edge

bed   wedge

red   ledge

Ted

Ned

fed

4 Write the word you hear.

1. _____   10. _____

2. _____

3. _____   11. _____

4. _____   12. _____

5. _____   13. _____

6. _____   14. _____

7. _____

8. _____

9. _____

5

Review Words

send
friend
letter

New Words

sent
went
wedding

6 Read the sentences.

1. Did Ed send letters to any of his friends?

   Yes, he sent a letter to his friend Ted.

2. Ned went out to the shed to get a pick.

3. Fred will cut the hedge for me.

4. Mother fed her children and sent them to bed.

   They went to bed at ten.

5. Meg wants a pretty wedding.

6. Ted went to the city in his red truck.

7. The bird makes a nest on the ledge.

8. Ned and Ted fed the pets.

9. He led them to the edge of the river.

10. Does your pup shed?

11. Bess sent Meg a pretty red dress.

12. When will Ned and Peg be wed?

    I want to go to the wedding and send a gift.

13. Fred sits on the edge of his bed.

14. Ed's neck gets red when he sits in the sun.

15. This wedge has a thin edge.

Practice 7-C: Adding Endings

1 To add -ing to a word that ends with -e, take off the -e and add -ing.

g i v ~~e~~ + i n g → giving

n u d g ~~e~~ + i n g → nudging

m a k ~~e~~ + i n g → making

2 Add -ing and read the word.

live _____

have _____

come _____

whistle _____

judge _____

like _____

3 Take off the -e, and add -ing to the word under the blank. Read the sentences.

1. Bess is _____ letters.
    write

2. Ed is _____ the pigs.
    judge

3. We are _____ apple jelly.
    make

4

Reviewing endings
Take off the -s ending, and read the word.

whips _____

sets _____

makes _____

puffs _____

quits _____

says _____

brings _____

tells _____

ticks _____

5

Reviewing endings
Add -ing to the word and fill in the blank. (For some words you may have to take off the -e. For some words you will have to double the last letter.) Read the sentences.

1. send   They are _____ you a check.

2. bet   Fred is _____ seventy cents.

3. dress   Peg is _____ her little kids.

4. come   Dick is _____ to dinner.

5. whistle Ted is _____ for the pup.

6. let   She is _____ us go to the city.

7. check   The men are _____ the truck.

8. rush   Jimmy is _____ to the shop.

9. take   The kids are _____ the cups to the sink.

6

Reviewing endings
Take off the -ing ending and write the root word. (For some words you may have to add a final -e. For some words you may have to take off a letter.)

making _____

shedding _____

writing _____

thinking _____

taking _____

hugging _____

bringing _____

dipping _____

coming _____

31

| i | bill | lit | pick | him | big | miss |
| e | bell | let | peck | hem | beg | mess |

---

1 Write the letter.

1. pig
   peg

   p __ g

2. will
   well

   w __ ll

3. bid
   bed

   b __ d

4. lid
   led

   l __ d

5. pin
   pen

   p __ n

---

2 Circle the word that you hear.

1. bit   bet
2. till   tell
3. chick   check
4. big   beg
5. wit   wet
6. him   hem
7. rid   red
8. lit   let
9. miss   mess
10. pick   peck
11. fill   fell
12. six   sex
13. tin   ten
14. pit   pet
15. bill   bell

---

3 Write the short vowel that you hear.

1. y __ t
2. h __ p
3. d __ ck
4. w __ ll
5. p __ g
6. w __ n
7. l __ d
8. th __ ck
9. r __ m
10. d __ n
11. p __ p
12. __ tch
13. s __ ll
14. k __ ss
15. f __ n

---

4 Circle the right word.

1. Did you get the ⎰ bill ⎱ for the dress?
                 bell

2. Jill wants ⎰ tin ⎱ apples.
             ten

3. She will ⎰ pick ⎱ the big ones.
            peck

4. I want to go with ⎰ him ⎱
                    hem

5. You will ⎰ miss ⎱ us when we go.
           mess

6. ⎰ Lit ⎱ me go with you.
     Let

u	bud	hum	lug	pup	duck	but
e	bed	hem	leg	pep	deck	bet

---

1 Write the letter.

1. chuck
check

ch __ ck

2. bug
beg

b __ g

3. pup
pep

p __ p

4. nut
net

n __ t

5. duck
deck

d __ ck

2 Circle the word that you hear.

1. hum   hem
2. bug   beg
3. jut   jet
4. muss   mess
5. bud   bed
6. pup   pep
7. duck   deck
8. lug   leg
9. but   bet
10. pun   pen
11. nut   net
12. dun   den
13. mush   mesh
14. chuck   check
15. bun   Ben

3 Write the short vowel that you hear.

1. p ___ t
2. b ___ ck
3. k ___ g
4. m ___ g
5. l ___ ss
6. b ___ t
7. t ___ b
8. p ___ ff
9. wh ___ n
10. b ___ s
11. f ___ d
12. r ___ sh
13. m ___ t
14. p ___ g
15. g ___ m

4 Circle the right word.

1. He is sick,   but / bet   he will get well.

2. Put some   mush / mesh   in the dish.

3.   Bun / Ben   and Rick are fishing.

4. The little girl has a   pup / pep.

5. Put some   nuts / nets   in the fudge.

6. The man sits in his   dun / den.

33

Practice 7-F: Review Lesson - Short e

1 Look at the picture and say the word.
Then fill in the right letter to make the word.

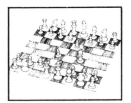

sh
___ess
ch

ck
ne ___
t

g
___ et
j

d
___ eck
p

d
she ___
ll

t
___ en
d

---

2 Circle the word that makes sense in the sentence.

1. Ned has not met my sister
   wet
   yet
   .

2. Fred yells, ''This shed is a
   less
   mess
   !''

3. Ed will cut the hedge for seventy
   cents
   sent
   .

4. Jess
   fell
   fed
   and hurt his leg.

5. The children
   beg
   peg
   Mother for a pet.

6. The vet will check my
   peck
   pet
   snake.

34

---

3 Look at the picture and say the word.
Then circle the right word.

1.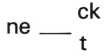
   peg   beg   leg   keg

2.
   yell   yet   shell   well

3.
   hem   then   hen   when

4.
   tell   tent   sent   ten

5.
   fed   shell   bed   shed

6.
   bet   bed   bell   hell

Practice 7-F: Review Lesson - Short e (continued)

4 Look at the picture and say the word. Then write the word under the picture.

 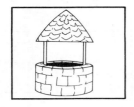  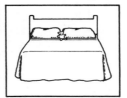  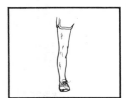

_____   _____   _____   _____   _____   _____

---

5 Circle all the words that are the same as the first.
Work from left to right.

peck	peck	pick	beck	peck	deck	peck	pet
ten	hen	ten	tent	then	tell	ten	net
less	chess	sell	less	led	less	let	mess
bed	bed	bet	deb	bell	bed	bud	led
wet	met	vet	wet	well	wet	met	yet
leg	led	leg	beg	get	lug	keg	leg
sell	sell	set	less	sell	well	cell	sell
them	then	them	hem	then	met	the	them

6 Read these sentences.

1. Peg tells me, "Ted is sick, but he will get well."

2. Yes, the men sell fresh eggs there.

3. Ken led his friends to the edge of the river.

4. Meg fed her kids. Then the kids went to bed.

5. Ed sits in the den looking at the TV set.

6. This pen has red ink. It sells for twelve cents.

7. If you make the best guess, you win the bet.

8. When Bess makes jelly, she lets the kids help her.

Practice 8-A: Word Family -at

1

bat

cat

-at

2 Write the letter or letters and say the word.

_____ at   ch _____ at

b _____ at   th _____ at

c _____ at   P _____ at

f _____ at

h _____ at

m _____ at

p _____ at

r _____ at

s _____ at

3 Read the words.

hat	rat
mat	cat
pat	sat
bat	
at	
fat	
that	
Pat	
chat	

4 Write the word you hear.

1. _____   10. _____

2. _____   11. _____

3. _____   12. _____

4. _____

5. _____

6. _____

7. _____

8. _____

9. _____

5

New Words

shall
take

Words from Skill Book 1

Cal

6 Read the sentences.

1. I will take this hat, not that one.

2. Pitch it, and I will hit it with the bat.

3. Bess and Pat like to chat on the telephone.

4. There is mud on that mat.

5. That cat is getting fat.

    Shall I take the cat to the vet?

6. Cal sat on my hat.

7. There are rats in that shed.

8. That dress will not fit if I get fat.

9. That bat has big wings.

10. Do not put fat in the sink.

11. Pat sells cats at her pet shop.

12. The pup sat on the mat.

13. Cal pats my hand.

14. Shall I take that bat to my brother?

15. She wants to chat with Cal.

16. Bud is fat, but he wants to be thin.

17. Shall we chat for a little bit?

Practice 8-B: Word Family -an

1

an

man

pan

-an

2 Write the letter or letters and say the word.

	an	th ____ an		
b ____ an		D ____ an		
c ____ an		J ____ an		
f ____ an		N ____ an		
m ____ an		V ____ an		
p ____ an				
r ____ an				
t ____ an				
v ____ an				

3 Read the words.

fan	Nan
ran	pan
man	Jan
van	ban
Dan	than
tan	
can	
Van	
an	

4 Write the word you hear.

1. _____   10. _____
2. _____   11. _____
3. _____   12. _____
4. _____   13. _____
5. _____   14. _____
6. _____
7. _____
8. _____
9. _____

5

Review Words

cannot
black
stand

New Words

as
by

Words from Skill Book 1

Ann

6 Read the sentences.

1. Jan is standing by the fan.

2. Put an egg into the pan of water.

3. Jan has a big tan van.

4. Nan does as well as she can.

5. Ann can fix the kitchen fan.

6. Dan ran as well as the other man.

7. Jan cut up an apple and put it in the pan.

8. Dan gets as much sun as Pat.

   But Dan is less tan than Pat.

10. Did you yell to him as he ran by?

11. There is a ban on fishing. You cannot do it.

12. The red van ran into the tan truck.

13. This set of pans sells for less than that set.

14. Get a can of black olives.

15. The man is so sick that he cannot stand up.

16. Can you take the big fan there in the van?

17. I sit out in the sun and get a tan.

18. You can set the dish by the pans.

1

Sam

-am

cab

-ab

2 Write the letter or letters and say the word.

	am	c	____	ab	
d	____ am	d	____	ab	
h	____ am	g	____	ab	
j	____ am	j	____	ab	
r	____ am	l	____	ab	
y	____ am	n	____	ab	
P	____ am	t	____	ab	
S	____ am				

3 Read the words.

jam	tab
Pam	jab
am	cab
Sam	dab
dam	nab
ram	gab
yam	lab
ham	

4 Write the word you hear.

1. _____   9. _____
2. _____   10. _____
3. _____   11. _____
4. _____   12. _____
5. _____   13. _____
6. _____   14. _____
7. _____   15. _____
8. _____

5

Review Words

back
family
building

New Words

keep

6 Read the sentences.

1. Sam takes a cab and gets there quickly.

2. Pam is fixing this ham for her family.

   They will have yams with the ham.

3. Do you want some jam?

   Yes, I will have a little dab.

4. Help me! I am in a jam!

5. I am building a big dam at the river.

   The dam will keep back the water.

6. Pam makes pills in the lab.

7. She puts on a pin, and it jabs her finger.

8. Did the cab ram into the truck?

9. They will nab the man when he gets there.

10. We get ham from pigs.

11. Pam is keeping tabs on her husband.

12. They are gabbing on the telephone.

13. We keep rats at the lab.

14. Cabs and trucks are in a jam on this street.

15. Pam and Jim are fishing at the dam.

1

back

Jack

-ack

wax

-ax

2 Write the letter or letters and say the word.

b ____ ack	sh ____ ack		
j ____ ack	J ____ ack		
l ____ ack			
p ____ ack		ax	
r ____ ack	t ____ ax		
s ____ ack	w ____ ax		
t ____ ack	M ____ ax		
bl ____ ack			
qu ____ ack			

3 Read the words.

tack	back
sack	quack
rack	
shack	tax
jack	wax
lack	ax
pack	Max
black	
Jack	

4 Write the word you hear.

1. _____   10. _____
2. _____   11. _____
3. _____
4. _____   12. _____
5. _____   13. _____
6. _____   14. _____
7. _____   15. _____
8. _____
9. _____

5

New Words

pay

car

6 Read the sentences.

1. Max will jack up his car.

2. We must pay our tax.

3. Go out to the shack and get the ax.

4. Did she pack her black dress?

5. Max is waxing his car.

6. Put the apples into a big sack.

7. Sam hits Jack on the back. Jack's back hurts.

8. Tack up this picture.

9. Jack will pay for the black car.

10. She puts the dress back on the rack.

11. I went to the shop for a box of tacks.

12. The jack is in the back of the car.

13. She lacks ten cents to pay for the gum.

14. Can you pay me back?

15. The ducks are quacking.

16. Jack gives me a pack of gum.

17. The can of olives is in that sack.

18. Jack put the car on the rack to fix it.

39

1

bag

tag

-ag

bad

dad

-ad

2 Write the letter or letters and say the word.

b _____ ag   _____ ad

g _____ ag   b _____ ad

l _____ ag   d _____ ad

n _____ ag   h _____ ad

r _____ ag   l _____ ad

s _____ ag   m _____ ad

t _____ ag   p _____ ad

w _____ ag   s _____ ad

sh _____ ag

3 Read the words.

tag	mad
gag	bad
lag	pad
bag	ad
nag	sad
wag	had
shag	dad
rag	lad
sag	

4 Write the word you hear.

1. _____   10. _____
2. _____   11. _____
3. _____   12. _____
4. _____   13. _____
5. _____   14. _____
6. _____   15. _____
7. _____   16. _____
8. _____   17. _____
9. _____

5

Review Words

seventy

6 Read the sentences.

1. Sam looks at the ads.

2. When Dad nags me, I get mad.

3. The shag rug has a pad under it.

4. They gag the man to keep him from yelling.

5. She is sad that she has no dad.

6. Look at the tags on that dress.

7. The bad man ran up to me. He had a gun!

8. Jack put the rags into a bag.

9. Your dress sags in the back.

10. Dan had bad cuts on his hands.

11. The ad says a bag of apples is seventy cents.

12. Kitty tags her sister on the back.

13. Pam rubs the wet dish with a rag.

14. A pen and a pad are by the telephone.

15. Did she pack her bags?

16. Mother gets mad if Dad just sits.

17. Jan is sad that the lad had to go.

18. Do not pat the cat when it is mad.

Practice 9-A: Word Families -ap, -as, -ass

1

cap
map
-ap

gas
-as

glass
-ass

2 Write the letter or letters and say the word.

c ____ ap   g ____ as

g ____ ap

l ____ ap   b ____ ass

m ____ ap   m ____ ass

n ____ ap   p ____ ass

s ____ ap   gl ____ ass

t ____ ap   gr ____ ass

y ____ ap

ch ____ ap

3 Read the words.

nap	gas
tap	
gap	mass
chap	grass
map	bass
lap	glass
yap	pass
cap	
sap	

4 Write the word you hear.

1. _____   10. _____

2. _____

3. _____   11. _____

4. _____   12. _____

5. _____   13. _____

6. _____   14. _____

7. _____   15. _____

8. _____

9. _____

5

Review Words

happy
laugh
basket
wind

New Words

ask
where

6 Read the sentences.

1. The children are taking a nap.

2. Where is that city on the map?

3. I have on my red cap.

4. I ask her, "Can you pass that car?"

5. Wind and water can chap your hands.

6. I am happy my car did not run out of gas.

7. We laugh at the pup when it yaps.

8. The black cat jumps out of my lap.

9. I ask him to pass me a glass of water.

10. Our family will go to mass at ten.

11. There are gaps where things are missing.

12. He gets up from his nap to cut the grass.

13. "Where do you go to fish for bass?" I ask.

14. He puts the gas cap back on the car.

15. I look at the map on my lap.

16. The children tap on the glass.

17. They will not let you in unless you have a pass.

18. He is happy to get this basket of apples.

41

1

rang

sang

-ang

thank

sank

-ank

2 Write the letter or letters and say the word.

b _____ ang   b _____ ank

f _____ ang   r _____ ank

g _____ ang   s _____ ank

h _____ ang   t _____ ank

r _____ ang   y _____ ank

s _____ ang   th _____ ank

              H _____ ank

3 Read the words.

hang	yank
rang	bank
sang	thank
gang	Hank
fang	tank
bang	rank
	sank

4 Write the word you hear.

1. _____   7. _____

2. _____   8. _____

3. _____   9. _____

4. _____   10. _____

5. _____   11. _____

6. _____   12. _____

                13. _____

5

Review Words

half

Words from Skill Book 1

number

6 Read the sentences.

1. Thanks for taking the check to the bank.

2. The telephone rang.

3. Hank is in a big gang of kids.

4. The snake has two big fangs.

5. Pam hangs up her dress.

6. The children sang and rang the bells.

7. Jan puts some fish in the tank.

8. The ship sank into the river.

9. Hang up that picture of our gang.

10. Hank yanks the bag out of my hands.

11. Thanks for cutting the grass.

12. Hank ranks number one in hits and runs.

13. A bell rang as the gang ran out of the bank.

14. I have half a tank of gas.

15. Jan cut her bangs.

16. Many pictures are hanging in the bank.

17. She sang to her kids when she put them to bed.

18. She bangs the pans when she is mad.

1

cash
mash
-ash
catch
match
-atch
path
math
-ath

2 Write the letter or letters and say the word.

	ash			atch
	ash	c	___	atch
c	___ ash	h	___	atch
d	___ ash	l	___	atch
g	___ ash	m	___	atch
h	___ ash	p	___	atch
l	___ ash			
m	___ ash	b	___	ath
r	___ ash	m	___	ath
s	___ ash	p	___	ath

3 Read the words.

dash	hatch
mash	patch
rash	catch
ash	match
hash	latch
sash	
lash	path
cash	bath
gash	math

4 Write the word you hear.

1. _____   10. _____
2. _____   11. _____
3. _____   12. _____
4. _____   13. _____
5. _____   14. _____
6. _____
7. _____   15. _____
8. _____   16. _____
9. _____   17. _____

5

Review Words

after
factory

New Words

work

6 Read the sentences.

1. After he works at the factory, he takes a bath.

2. Jan has a red rash on her hands.

3. He lit a match.

4. My pup runs up the path after a cat.

   I dash after him, but I cannot catch him.

5. Mash some yams to have with the hash.

6. Dan likes to work with numbers and do math.

   He works at the bank cashing checks.

7. The chicks will hatch from the eggs.

8. Her red hat does not match her red dress.

9. If I can catch that pup, I will give it a bath.

10. Patch the rip in the tan dress.

11. The glass cut a big gash in his hand.

12. That dress has a pretty sash with it.

    Will you pay cash for the dress?

13. He wants to catch some fish.

14. Sam ran up the path to the glass factory.

15. The latch will not catch.

43

Practice 9-D: Adding Endings

1

Adding -y to words

w i n d + y → windy

Bill _____

itch _____

hand _____

mess _____

puff _____

2

Label the last three letters.
Then write the word with -y.

   v c c + y

j u m p + y → jumpy

mush _____

hill _____

dress _____

luck _____

fish _____

3

Label the last three letters.
Then write the word with -y.

   c v c + c + y

K e n + n + y → Kenny

gum _____

bag _____

nut _____

fun _____

Peg _____

4

Label the last three letters
with VCC or CVC. Then write
the word with -y.

Tim _____

sun _____

grass _____

dad _____

bud _____

fuss _____

5

Add -y and read the word.
Double the last letter
if you have to.

Pat _____

glass _____

Dan _____

pup _____

chunk _____

Sam _____

Ted _____

mud _____

6

Take off -y and write
the root word.

lucky _____

chilly _____

witty _____

puffy _____

runny _____

messy _____

handy _____

chatty _____

7

Reviewing endings
Circle all the words that are the same as the first one.

puff	puffs	puff	puffing	puff	puffy	puffs	puff
bags	bag	baggy	bags	bagging	bags	baggy	bag
chilly	chilly	chills	chilling	chilly	chill	chills	chilling
tap	taps	tap	tapping	taps	tap	tapping	tap
picking	pick	picks	picking	picky	picks	picking	picky

44

Practice 9-E: Contrasting Short Vowels a and e

a	bag	fad	pack	sat	than	lad
e	beg	fed	peck	set	then	led

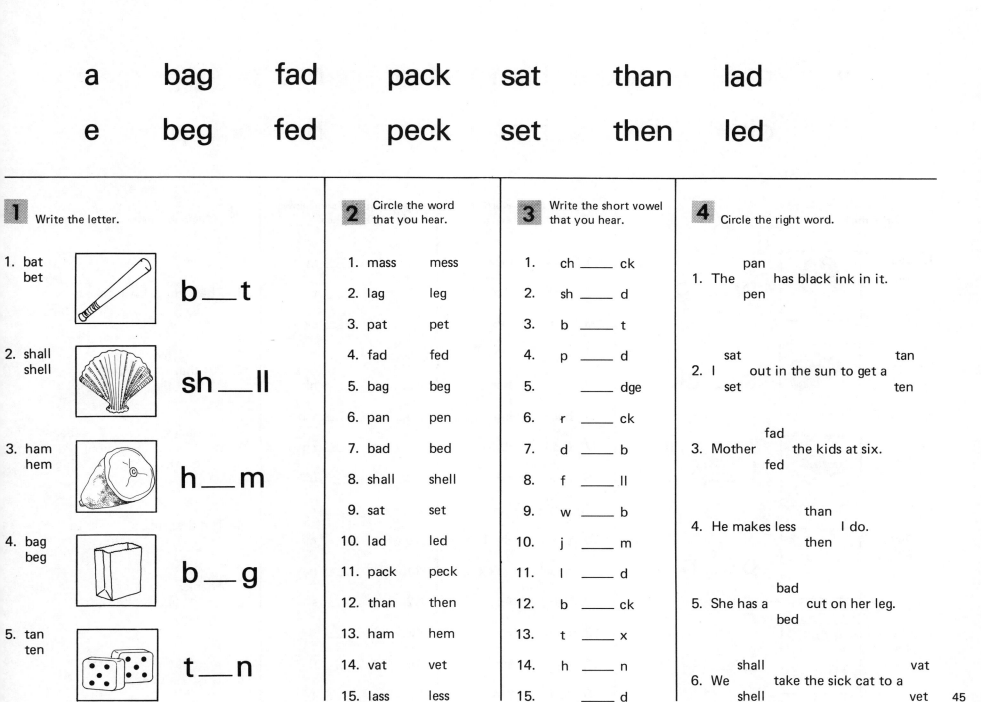

1 Write the letter.

1. bat
   bet

   b __ t

2. shall
   shell

   sh __ ll

3. ham
   hem

   h __ m

4. bag
   beg

   b __ g

5. tan
   ten

   t __ n

2 Circle the word that you hear.

1. mass   mess
2. lag   leg
3. pat   pet
4. fad   fed
5. bag   beg
6. pan   pen
7. bad   bed
8. shall   shell
9. sat   set
10. lad   led
11. pack   peck
12. than   then
13. ham   hem
14. vat   vet
15. lass   less

3 Write the short vowel that you hear.

1. ch ___ ck
2. sh ___ d
3. b ___ t
4. p ___ d
5. ___ dge
6. r ___ ck
7. d ___ b
8. f ___ ll
9. w ___ b
10. j ___ m
11. l ___ d
12. b ___ ck
13. t ___ x
14. h ___ n
15. ___ d

4 Circle the right word.

1. The pan / pen has black ink in it.

2. I sat / set out in the sun to get a tan / ten

3. Mother fad / fed the kids at six.

4. He makes less than / then I do.

5. She has a bad / bed cut on her leg.

6. We shall / shell take the sick cat to a vat / vet

45

a	dad	lack	ham	fan	bat	nap
i	did	lick	him	fin	bit	nip

---

1 Write the letter.

1. wag
   wig

w __ g

2. sack
   sick

s __ ck

3. lap
   lip

l __ p

4. pan
   pin

p __ n

5. bag
   big

b __ g

2 Circle the word that you hear.

1. pack   pick
2. dam   dim
3. had   hid
4. fat   fit
5. tack   tick
6. bag   big
7. dash   dish
8. rap   rip
9. mass   miss
10. thank   think
11. quack   quick
12. lad   lid
13. rang   ring
14. sap   sip
15. pan   pin

3 Write the short vowel that you hear.

1. r ___ m
2. h ___ t
3. s ___ ck
4. t ___ n
5. l ___ nk
6. h ___ tch
7. s ___ ng
8. l ___ b
9. p ___ t
10. r ___ nk
11. b ___ n
12. h ___ s
13. b ___ d
14. t ___ p
15. s ___ t

4 Circle the right word.

1. The little girl will take a ___.   nap / nip

2. Put the ___ on that.   lad / lid

3. Be ___ ! Pack your ___ !   quack quick / bag big

4. The dress has a ___ in it.   rap / rip

5. ___ you for the gift.   Thank / Think

6. This ___ does not ___ .   hat fat / hit fit

46

a	ran	tag	ham	rat	cab	sang
u	run	tug	hum	rut	cub	sung

---

1 Write the letter.

1. fan
   fun

   f __ n

2. tab
   tub

   t __ b

3. hat
   hut

   h __ t

4. tack
   tuck

   t __ ck

5. bad
   bud

   b __ d

2 Circle the word that you hear.

1. back   buck
2. hag   hug
3. cat   cut
4. mad   mud
5. pan   pun
6. lack   luck
7. bank   bunk
8. bat   but
9. ram   rum
10. cap   cup
11. rag   rug
12. badge budge
13. hang   hung
14. sack   suck
15. rash   rush

3 Write the short vowel that you hear.

1. n ____ b
2. b ____ zz
3. m ____ ss
4. b ____ n
5. j ____ g
6. c ____ ff
7. r ____ g
8. g ____ sh
9. p ____ ck
10. l ____ g
11. s ____ nk
12. s ____ p
13. h ____ sh
14. b ____ g
15. m ____ tch

4 Circle the right word.

1. Mother yells when she gets ____ .   mad / mud

2. Dad gives his little girl a ____ .   hag / hug

3. Jan takes a ____ to the shop.   cab / cub

4. Put the rags in this ____ .   sack / suck

5. Bill must ____ to get the bus.   rash / rush

6. Jack works in the ____ .   bank / bunk

47

Practice 9-H: Review Lesson - Short a

1 Look at the picture and say the word.
Then fill in the right letter to make the word.

sa ___ g
___ ck

v
f ___ an

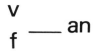

ca ___ t
___ n

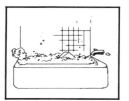

b
p ___ ath

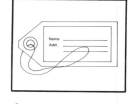

l
t ___ ag

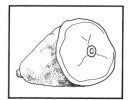

ha ___ ng
___ m

---

2 Circle the word that makes sense in the sentence.

1. Bring the fan   back / bag   after you fix it.

2. The fish   sang / sank   in the tank.

3. Dad   rags / nags   at me to do my math.

4. Hank   sat / fat   on the grass by the path.

5. I am   pad / sad   to see Nan go.

6. Jack can pay the   tack / tax   So can his   bad / dad

3 Look at the picture and say the word.
Then circle the right word.

1.    fan   van   ran   vat

2.    tax   tank   tag   tack

3.    fat   sat   hat   that

4.    cab   gab   cap   nab

5.    bang   bank   bag   ban

6.   grass   gas   glass   pass

48

4 Look at the picture and say the word. Then write the word under the picture.

  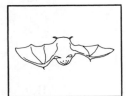   

_____ _____ _____ _____ _____ _____

---

5 Circle all the words that are the same as the first.
Work from left to right.

nap	pan	map	nap	rap	nag	nap	nab
sag	sad	sag	gag	sap	gas	wag	sag
mad	map	mad	had	dam	mad	mud	mad
ban	bang	nab	ban	pan	ban	bank	bun
dab	dab	dad	bad	dab	gab	bad	dab
pat	pal	tap	pat	bat	path	pet	pat
mash	mash	math	mash	mass	mash	sham	hash
lag	lap	lag	lad	gal	tag	lag	hag

6 Read these sentences.

1. My van ran out of gas. I will have to take a cab.

2. Jan packs a hat and a tan dress in her bag.

3. Ann Black pays cash when she shops.

   She gets a ham, a can of yams, and a sack of apples.

4. Sam had a chat with the man at the bank.

5. Pam gets mad if the cat jumps into her lap.

6. The gang sang at the mass. Did Pat thank them?

7. I will catch up to Dan's car and then pass it.

1

hot

not

-ot

on

Don

-on

2 Write the letter or letters and say the word.

c ＿＿ ot   sh ＿＿ ot

d ＿＿ ot   sp ＿＿ ot

g ＿＿ ot

h ＿＿ ot   on

j ＿＿ ot   D ＿＿ on

l ＿＿ ot   R ＿＿ on

n ＿＿ ot

p ＿＿ ot

t ＿＿ ot

3 Read the words.

dot   jot

pot   tot

cot

spot   Ron

hot   Don

not   on

got

shot

lot

4 Write the word you hear.

1. ＿＿＿＿＿＿   10. ＿＿＿＿＿＿

2. ＿＿＿＿＿＿   11. ＿＿＿＿＿＿

3. ＿＿＿＿＿＿

4. ＿＿＿＿＿＿   12. ＿＿＿＿＿＿

5. ＿＿＿＿＿＿   13. ＿＿＿＿＿＿

6. ＿＿＿＿＿＿   14. ＿＿＿＿＿＿

7. ＿＿＿＿＿＿

8. ＿＿＿＿＿＿

9. ＿＿＿＿＿＿

5

Review Words

building
Chan
doctor
Dr.
head
John
Molly
office

6 Read the sentences.

1. Don does not work a lot.

2. Molly's head is hot.

   She has red spots.

   The doctor will give Molly a shot.

3. Don has two cots in his tent.

4. Pam has on a dress with pink dots.

   Did she get a spot on her dress?

5. It got hot in the doctor's office.

6. Ron does not have any pots and pans.

7. He jots the words on a pad.

8. Ron shot a lot of ducks with his gun.

9. I sing to the little tots.

10. Did Don work out in the hot sun?

11. Dr. Chan says lots of men got sick.

12. That pot is hot. Do not pick it up.

13. She got a letter from John.

14. Ron will put up a building on that lot.

1

top

shop

-op

2 Write the letter or letters and say the word.

c ——— op

h ——— op

m ——— op

p ——— op

t ——— op

dr ——— op

st ——— op

sh ——— op

ch ——— op

3 Read the words.

mop

chop

top

cop

shop

stop

pop

drop

hop

4 Write the word you hear.

1. ———————

2. ———————

3. ———————

4. ———————

5. ———————

6. ———————

7. ———————

8. ———————

9. ———————

5

Review Words

doll
dollar

New Words

every
corn

6 Read the sentences.

1. Mop up every drop of water!

2. Stop the car! I want to get out!

3. Do not drop your dishes in the sink.

4. Jim asks Pat to chop up the eggs.

5. At the top of the hill, a girl ran into the street.

   A red car hit the girl, but it did not stop.

   The cops are looking for the car.

   They are stopping every red car in the city.

6. Her hands are wet, and she drops a dish.

7. The cops are keeping the men back.

8. Every kid likes to pop corn.

   The corn pops when it gets hot.

   Keep the top on the pan when the corn pops.

9. She pays six dollars for the doll in the shop.

10. Molly is chopping up nuts for the fudge.

11. After Bill fell, he had to hop on one leg.

12. If I drop this glass of pop, I must mop it up.

13. Ann is shopping for ham, chops, and corn.

51

Practice 10-C: Word Families -ob, -od

1

Bob

job

-ob

rod

-od

2 Write the letter or letters and say the word.

c ___ ob   c ___ od

j ___ ob   n ___ od

m ___ ob   p ___ od

r ___ ob   r ___ od

s ___ ob   G ___ od

B ___ ob

3 Read the words.

rob	rod
mob	nod
job	cod
sob	God
Bob	pod
cob	

4 Write the word you hear.

1. _____   7. _____

2. _____   8. _____

3. _____   9. _____

4. _____   10. _____

5. _____   11. _____

6. _____

5

Review Words

Tom
lock

New Words

Mom

Words from Skill Book 1

Robert

6 Read the sentences.

1. Robert wants some corn on the cob.

2. Mom will hang the wet socks on racks.

3. Robert nods his head at Mom.

4. Bob is looking at TV.

5. Mom tells her children that God is good.

   She tells them to thank God.

6. Kim will give him a fishing rod.

   He wants to fish for cod.

7. A man robs the bank.

8. Bob got a job in the city.

   Then Tom said to Bob, "Help me get a job."

9. Pam is sad. She is sobbing.

10. There is a mob at the factory.

    The men and women want jobs.

11. We are having corn on the cob for dinner.

12. Bob asks Pat, "Will you go with me?"

    Pat nods her head.

13. Tom locks the shop so that no one can rob it.

Practice 11-A: Word Families -ock, -ox

1

lock

rock

-ock

box

-ox

2 Write the letter or letters and say the word.

d ____ ock   ox

l ____ ock   b ____ ox

m ____ ock   f ____ ox

r ____ ock

s ____ ock

cl ____ ock

sh ____ ock

3 Read the words.

rock   box

lock   ox

shock   fox

dock

mock

clock

sock

4 Write the word you hear.

1. _____   8. _____

2. _____   9. _____

3. _____   10. _____

4. _____

5. _____

6. _____

7. _____

5

Review Words

better
father
said
skirt
stopped
was
were

New Words

o'clock

6 Read the sentences.

1. Pat will get a shock if you tell her that!

2. The kids pick up pretty rocks at the river.

3. He ran by as quick as a fox.

4. The ship will be at the dock at ten o'clock.

5. Jill put the skirts and socks in the box.

6. They were sitting on a big rock by the river.

7. Is there a clock in the kitchen?

8. The fox got the hen. I shot at the fox.

9. That man is as big as an ox.

10. Don locks up the shop at five o'clock.

11. Father said to his little son, "Put your socks on."

12. I got a shock when I was fixing the TV.

13. Jan rocks her little girl.

14. My clock has stopped. Is it six o'clock yet?

15. Tom can box better than Bob.

16. This lock works better than the other one.

53

Practice 11-B: Adding -ed or -d to Action Words to Show Past Action

1 Adding -ed to VCC words

V C C + e d

w a n t + e d → wanted

b u r n + e d → burned

h e l p + e d → helped

Add -ed and read the word.

work _____

jump _____

ask _____

hunt _____

2 Adding -ed to CVC words

C V C + C + e d

c h a t + t + ed → chatted

b e g + g + ed → begged

s h o p + p + ed → shopped

Add -ed and read the word.

sob _____

tap _____

hop _____

spot _____

3 Adding -d to words that end in -e

l i v e + d → lived

l i k e + d → liked

Add -d and read the word.

judge _____

whistle _____

nudge _____

live _____

4

Add -d or -ed and read the words. Double the last letter if you have to.

pass _____

tap _____

like _____

rock _____

chat _____

burn _____

yank _____

pat _____

5

Add -ed or -d to the word and fill in the blank. Double the last letter if you have to. Read the sentence.

1. check   I _____ my work.

2. live   We _____ on a hill.

3. lock   Molly _____ the box.

4. nod   Father _____ his head.

5. like   Jack _____ his work.

6. rob   Two men _____ the shop.

7. hatch   The chicks _____ .

8. rub   Mom _____ my back.

9. pass   That car_____ me.

10. stop   The cop _____ the car.

11. can   Mom _____ the corn.

12. mess   They_____ up the kitchen.

13. chop   I _____ the olives.

14. shock   Bob _____ me.

15. beg   The pup sat up and _____ .

16. match   Her dress _____ her bag.

a	an	cab	sack	tap	hat
o	on	cob	sock	top	hot

---

1 Write the letter.

1. map
   mop

   m __ p

2. rack
   rock

   r __ ck

3. pat
   pot

   p __ t

4. cab
   cob

   c __ b

5. ax
   ox

   __ x

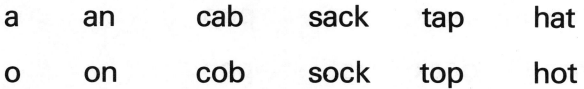

---

2 Circle the word that you hear.

1. rat   rot
2. cap   cop
3. pad   pod
4. shack   shock
5. jab   job
6. sad   sod
7. cat   cot
8. tap   top
9. rack   rock
10. mad   mod
11. ax   ox
12. hat   hot
13. lack   lock
14. Dan   Don
15. chap   chop

---

3 Write the short vowel that you hear.

1. c ____ n
2. H ____ nk
3. l ____ p
4. m ____ b
5. t ____ ck
6. c ____ sh
7. h ____ p
8. r ____ d
9. t ____ b
10. p ____ t
11. r ____ n
12. t ____ t
13. s ____ ck
14. s ____ p
15. m ____ d

---

4 Circle the right word.

1. The   cap   runs after the men.
           cop

2. I have a good   jab   at the factory.
                    job

3. A red dress is hanging   an   rack
                        the
                             on   rock   .

4. Jan is happy, not   sad   .
                        sod

5. Your   cat   is sitting on my   hat   .
           cot   hot

6. He will   chap   that with an   ax   .
              chop   ox

55

u	cub	hut	duck	rut	pup
o	cob	hot	dock	rot	pop

---

1 Write the letter.

1. luck
   lock

   l__ck

2. nut
   not

   n__t

3. cup
   cop

   c__p

4. suck
   sock

   s__ck

5. cut
   cot
   c__t

2 Circle the word that you hear.

1. nut   not
2. shuck   shock
3. rub   rob
4. hut   hot
5. cut   cot
6. sub   sob
7. run   Ron
8. mud   mod
9. shut   shot
10. pup   pop
11. jut   jot
12. hunk   honk
13. duck   dock
14. cub   cob
15. suck   sock

3 Write the short vowel that you hear.

1. m ___ m
2. t ___ ck
3. g ___ t
4. b ___ t
5. j ___ t
6. r ___ ck
7. j ___ g
8. r ___ t
9. d ___ ck
10. m ___ p
11. h ___ t
12. r ___ n
13. p ___ t
14. c ___ p
15. ch ___ nk

4 Circle the right word.

1. That man wants to ___ the shop.
   rub
   rob

2. Dr. Hill will give Tom a ___
   shut
   shot

3. The ___ jumps into the mud.
   pup
   pop

4. It was ___ in the kitchen.
   hut
   hot

5. Put the ___ in the sink.
   cup
   cop

6. He does ___ have good ___
   nut   luck
   not   lock

Practice 11-E: Review Lesson - Short O

1 Look at the picture and say the word.
Then fill in the right letter to make the word.

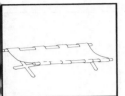

g
___ ot
c

        b
mo ___
        p

r
l ___ ock

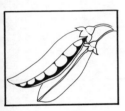

       d
po ___
       t

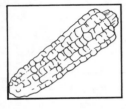

       b
co ___
       d

ch
sh ___ op

---

2 Circle the word that makes sense in the sentence.

1. We must   stop / spot   the car!

2. We will have corn on the   cob / cop   .

3. The   lots / tots   take naps at two o'clock.

4. What a shock! Bob is quitting his   jot / job   !

5. Get rid of the   robbing / rotting   apples.

6. Tom works at his dad's   shot / shop   .

3 Look at the picture and say the word.
Then circle the right word.

1.    chop   mop   hop   shop

2.    lock   rock   sock   lot

3. 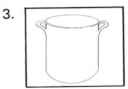   dot   spot   pod   pot

4. 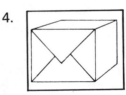   fox   box   pox   pot

5.    cob   cod   cop   cot

6.    hot   lot   not   rot

57

Practice 11-E: Review Lesson - Short O (continued)

4 Look at the picture and say the word. Then write the word under the picture.

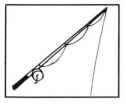     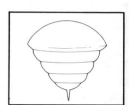

_____   _____   _____   _____   _____   _____

5 Circle all the words that are the same as the first.
Work from left to right.

got	got	jot	tot	get	pot	got	cot
pot	cot	pot	jot	pet	pot	got	pot
top	pot	stop	top	tot	top	hop	pot
god	gob	god	dot	pod	god	cod	god
lock	lock	lick	clock	lock	lack	luck	lock
spot	pot	stop	spot	shot	pots	spot	stop
box	fox	ox	box	ox	box	fox	fox
nod	rod	nod	don	nod	not	mod	nod

6 Read these sentences.

1. Ron pays half a dollar for a can of pop.

2. Bob is at the dock. He is fishing with his rod.

3. Don has not had the top job.

4. John shot at the fox.

5. Ron does not lock up the cash box in the shop.

    A man robs the shop.

6. The mob was mad at the cops.

7. Molly drops a cup of water. Mom mops it up.

Practice 12: Adding -es to Words

1

-s
-x
-sh
-ch

+**es**, not **s**

k i s s + e s → kisses
f i x + e s → fixes
d i s h + e s → dishes
m a t c h + e s → matches

2 *-s* **Words**
Add *-es* to these words.
Fill in the blanks. Read the sentences.

1. kiss   Jim _____ his girl.

2. guess   I will give you two _____ .

3. fuss   Ed _____ when he is sick.

4. mess   My son _____ up the tent.

5. glass   I like my pink _____ .

6. dress   Pam gets two new _____ .

7. pass   A big car _____ my car.

3 *-x* **Words**
Add *-es* to these words.
Fill in the blanks. Read the sentences.

1. ax   We have two _____ in the shed.

2. box   She sent me two _____ of fudge.

3. fix   Jan _____ a duck dinner.

4. tax   We pay so many _____ !

5. fox   The _____ ran after the hens.

6. mix   Meg _____ the chip dip.

7. wax   Dan _____ his new truck.

4

-sh **Words**
Add *-es* to these words.
Fill in the blanks. Read the sentences.

1. dash   Kim _____ after the pup.

2. wish   She _____ for a black car.

3. ash   The shed burns to _____ .

4. rush   Mom _____ out of the kitchen.

5. cash   Tom _____ his check.

6. dish   Jack brings the _____ to the sink.

7. mash   Nan _____ the yams.

8. fish   Bud _____ in the river.

5

-ch **Words**
Add *-es* to these words.
Fill in the blanks. Read the sentences.

1. pitch   Fred _____ to us.

2. hatch   The chick _____ out of the egg.

3. ditch   The men are digging big _____ .

4. match   Take the _____ from the kids.

5. rich   He wants _____ .

6. patch   Bess puts some _____ on her skirt.

7. catch   Ken _____ the pup.

8. itch   Chuck's hand _____ .

6

Take off the *-es* and write the root word. Read the words.

catches _____

rushes _____

mixes _____

passes _____

ditches _____

wishes _____

taxes _____

kisses _____

rashes _____ 59

Practice 13-A: Adding -er or -r to Words

1

Adding -er to VCC words

V C C + e r
t h i c k + e r → **thicker**

Add -er and read the words.

rich _____

black _____

2

Adding -er to CVC words

C V C + C + e r
t h i n + n + e r → **thinner**

Add -er and read the words.

hot _____

big _____

3

Just add -r to words that end with -e.

l a r g e + r → **larger**

Add -r and read the words.

little _____

large _____

4

Add -er or -r to the word.
Double the last letter if you
have to. Read the word.

fresh _____

wet _____

large _____

sick _____

red _____

dark _____

sad _____

quick _____

rich _____

little _____

5

Add -er or -r to the word and fill in the blank.
Double the last letter if you have to.
Read the sentence.

1. rich   He is _____ than I am.

2. hot   It is getting much _____.

3. mad   He got _____ when I stopped him.

4. large   This park is _____ than the other one.

5. thin   This kid is _____ than that kid.

6. dark   Your dress is a _____ red than my dress.

7. fresh   This egg is _____ than that egg.

8. wet   Take this rag. It is _____ than that one.

9. big   John is _____ than his brother.

10. hard   This work is much _____ to do.

11. quick   The cat is _____ than the rat.

12. up   I had a nap on the _____ bunk.

13. thick   This mix is getting _____.

14. fat   Dad is _____ than Mom.

15. red   Jill is getting _____ in the sun.

16. sick   Tom was _____ than his brother.

Practice 13-B: Adding -er or -r to Action Words

1 Adding -er or -r to action words

This part starts the car.
It is a starter.

Jack sits with kids.
He is a sitter.

Pat writes for the paper.
She is a writer.

2 Adding -er or -r to action words

V C C + e r
s t a r t + e r → starter

C V C + C + e r
s i t + t + e r → sitter

+ r
w r i t e + r → writer

3 Add -er or -r to the words. Double the last letter if you have to. Read the words.

sell _____ build _____

hit _____ farm _____

help _____ win _____

make _____ think _____

run _____ whistle _____

4

Add -er or -r to the word. Double the last letter if you have to.
Read the sentences.

1. sing   Billy wants to be a _____ .

2. work   The factory _____ likes her job.

3. win   Peg is the _____ !

4. bat   The _____ hurt his arm.

5. write   That _____ is very witty.

6. rock   Jan is sitting on the _____ .

7. rob   The cop will catch the _____ .

8. bid   He sells the TV to the top _____ .

9. bank   The _____ looks at the checks.

10. kill   Get some bug _____ at the shop.

5

Some other words have double letters and -er.
But the -er is part of the word. It is not an ending that is added.
Read the words. Use them to fill in the blanks. Read the sentences.

1. suffer   If pets do not have water, they _____ .

2. copper   They make the pans out of _____ .

3. ladder   The man is standing on a _____ .

4. butter   I put half a cup of _____ in the fudge.

5. hammer   Hit the tack with a _____ .

6. dinner   We are having ham for _____ .

7. letter   Jim writes Pat a _____ .

8. litter   Pick that up! Do not _____ .

9. matter   It does not _____ when he comes.

10. summer   It gets very hot in the _____ .

61

Practice 13-C: Endings for Words that End with Consonant +y

1 Adding -ing

Just add -ing.

c a r r y + i n g → carrying

Add -ing to the word and fill in the blank. Read the sentence.

carry	The men are _____ a TV set.
hurry	Dr. Chan is _____ to her office.

Take off the ending. Write the root word.

hurrying _____

carrying _____

---

2 Adding -ed

Change y to i, and then add -ed.

m a r r y

m a r r i + e d → married

Add -ed to the word and fill in the blank. Read the sentence.

marry	My sister _____ Ken.
carry	He _____ the pup to the vet.

Take off the ending. Write the root word.

carried _____

married _____

---

3 Adding -es to action words

Change y to i, and then add -es.

h u r r y

h u r r i + e s → hurries

Add -es to the word and fill in the blank. Read the sentence.

hurry	Peg _____ to work.
carry	Rick _____ the sack on his arm.

Take off the ending. Write the root word.

carries _____

hurries _____

---

4 Adding -es to show there is more than one

Change y to i, and then add -es.

c i t y

c i t i + e s → cities

Add -es to the word and fill in the blank. Read the sentence.

puppy	Jill has six little _____!
lily	The garden shop sells _____.
jelly	Pam sells jams and _____.

Take off the ending. Write the root word.

factories _____

families _____

cities _____

---

5 Adding -er

Change y to i, and then add -er.

l u c k y

l u c k i + e r → luckier

Add -er to the word and fill in the blank. Read the sentence.

lucky	John was _____ than I was.
happy	I am _____ if you are with me.
pretty	Liz is _____ than her sister.

Take off the ending. Write the root word.

messier _____

prettier _____

sunnier _____

Practice 14-A: Compound Words

1   Look at these compound words:

sunset	<u>sun</u>	<u>set</u>	forget	<u>for</u>	<u>get</u>	checkout	<u>check</u>	<u>out</u>
anyone	<u>any</u>	<u>one</u>	dishrag	<u>dish</u>	<u>rag</u>	backpack	<u>back</u>	<u>pack</u>

2   Put the two words together to make a compound word. Read the word.

red head	_____	bath tub	_____	back lash	_____
stand by	_____	cat nip	_____	any where	_____
street car	_____	hand out	_____	patch work	_____
up keep	_____	pot luck	_____	sun bath	_____

3   Find the two smaller words in each compound word. Write them in the blanks. Read the smaller words and the compound words.

jackpot	_____ _____	dishwater	_____ _____	comeback	_____ _____
everyone	_____ _____	catfish	_____ _____	dugout	_____ _____
suntan	_____ _____	checkup	_____ _____	pigpen	_____ _____
outfit	_____ _____	makeup	_____ _____	something	_____ _____

4   Make compound words. Match each word on the left with a word on the right.
Write the compound word in the blank. The first one is done for you.

pop	<u>**popcorn**</u>	work	for	_____	back	pad	_____	out
bath	_____	corn	up	_____	fish	sun	_____	lock
net	_____	what	quarter	_____	give	drop	_____	stand
some	_____	tub	shell	_____	hill	under	_____	burn

63

Practice 14-B: Two-syllable Words

1 The big words below have been divided into syllables. Using what you have learned about sounding out words, sound out the syllables and figure out each word.

public   /**pub** lic/   rabbit   /**rab** bit/   model   /**mod** el/   admit   /ad **mit**/

2 Read the word first. Then read the sentence.

1. rabbit   /**rab** bit/   The <u>rabbit</u> is in the garden.

2. sudden   /**sud** den/   Did the bus make a <u>sudden</u> stop?

3. public   /**pub** lic/   Anyone can come to a <u>public</u> park.

4. napkin   /**nap** kin/   He has a <u>napkin</u> on his lap.

5. model   /**mod** el/   Peg will <u>model</u> the pretty dress.

6. limit   /**lim** it/   Jim's car is going less than the <u>limit</u>.

7. discuss   /dis **cuss**/   They met to <u>discuss</u> it.

3 Read the word. Fill in the blank. Read the sentence.

1. happen   /**hap** pen/   Did that _____ at work?

2. picnic   /**pic** nic/   I will carry the _____ basket.

3. witness   /**wit** ness/   The _____ looks at the robber.

4. fabric   /**fab** ric/   I cannot get the spot out of the _____ .

5. finish   /**fin** ish/   You can go after you _____ the work.

6. habit   /**hab** it/   She sucks on her finger. It is a bad _____

7. admit   /ad **mit**/   The robber did not _____ that he did it.

4 A Working Woman   **Review Word:** heard   **New Word:** love

Nan was up on a ladder with a hammer in her hand.
She heard a car stop.
It was her best friend Jim, coming to pick her up from work.

"It is so hot I want to go to the park for a picnic dinner," Nan said.
"This job is hard work, but I have to admit the pay is good."

Jim did not like to discuss jobs and pay.
He did not have a job yet, but he was looking for one.
He liked to fix cars and trucks.

"Shut up!" he said. "It makes me mad to think you will have to pay the bills if we get married!"

Nan stopped her work and hugged Jim.
Nan said, "You will get a job! You are better at fixing cars than anyone!"

Jim hugged her and kissed her.
"Forgive me for getting so mad," he said.
"It just upsets me to think you are working and I have no job."

Nan said, "That is the limit! If I have no job and you are working, do you think I will not love you then? Loving you is a good habit. I do not want to stop!"

Jim laughed. "I do love you so!" he said.
"You make everything so funny! I am lucky that you love me.
Does it matter if I make less than you?
I will make it up to you. When I have a good job, you can just be with our kids."

"If I want to?" asked Nan.
"If you want to," said Jim.